# Times Tables Tests
## Book 2 Answers

Schofield & Sims

# Teacher's notes

### Introduction
Schofield & Sims Times Tables Book 2 provides differentiated practice tests in this key area of maths, to be administered regularly. It contains 24 tests grouped into two sections which each contain 12 tests. Each section ends with a Progress Test which summarises the content of the section.

### Parts A, B and C
Each of the 24 tests appears on a single page and is divided into three parts (A, B and C). This division enables you to to ensure that differentiation takes place: Part A uses straight forward notation where possible and part B uses simple language so that children with reading difficulties will not be disadvantaged. It is suggested that one test is taken each week and that Parts A, B and C are set on separate days. Since speed with accuracy is important, a time limit of 10 minutes per part is recommended.

### Answering the test questions
The books are presented in a one-per-child format, so that answers are written in the blanks. If children are allowed rough paper for working out, remember that their responses will be slower.

### Marking
When the children have completed a test, read out the answers as the children mark their own work, or give them the answer books to refer to themselves.

Published by Schofield and Sims Limited,
Dogley Mill, Fenay Bridge, Huddersfield HD8 0NQ, UK
Telephone 01484 607080
www.schofieldandsims.co.uk

First published in 2008

Copyright © Schofield and Sims Limited 2008

Authors: Steve Mills and Hilary Koll
(contact@cmeprojects.com)

Steve Mills and Hilary Koll have asserted their moral rights under the Copyright, Designs and Patents Act, 1988, to be identified as the authors of this work.

British Library Catalogue in Publication Data

A catalogue record for this book is available from the British Library.

Edited by Sue Gardner (susan.gardner1166@btinternet.com)

Design by Ledgard Jepson

Printed in the UK by Wyndeham Gait Ltd, Grimsby, Lincolnshire

ISBN 978 07217 1137 9

# Contents

The following is a short synopsis of the contents of the tests, indicating the order in which topics are introduced and their coverage.

Multiplication relating to the 0, 1, 2, 3, 4, 5 and
  10 times tables (including reversals)
Division facts relating to the 0, 1, 2, 3, 4, 5 and
  10 times tables
Doubling and halving
Use of $+$, $-$, $\times$ and $\div$ signs
$\frac{1}{2}$, $\frac{1}{3}$, $\frac{1}{4}$, $\frac{1}{5}$, $\frac{1}{10}$ and practical applications
Coins, sums of money and conversions
Units of measurement for length, mass, capacity, time
Perimeters and areas of shapes

Multiplication relating to the 0, 1, 2, 3, 4, 5, 6, 7,
  8, 9 and 10 times tables
Division facts relating to the 0, 1, 2, 3, 4, 5, 6, 7,
  8, 9 and 10 times tables and division with remainders
Doubling and halving
Use of $+$, $-$, $\times$ and $\div$ signs
$\frac{1}{2}$, $\frac{1}{3}$, $\frac{1}{4}$, $\frac{1}{5}$, $\frac{1}{6}$, $\frac{1}{7}$, $\frac{1}{8}$, $\frac{1}{9}$, $\frac{1}{10}$ and
  practical applications
Coins, sums of money and conversions
Units of measurement for length, mass, capacity, time
Perimeters and areas of shapes

Times tables up to $10 \times 10$
Division facts relating to the times tables up to $10 \times 10$
Multiplication of multiples of 10 and 100 relating to times
  tables up to $10 \times 10$
Division of multiples of 10 and 100 relating to times tables
Use of $+$, $-$, $\times$ and $\div$ signs
Squares of numbers
Finding fractions of numbers using multiplication and division
Perimeters and areas of shapes
Coins, sums of money and conversions
Units of measurement for length, mass, capacity, time

Multiplication tables up to $12 \times 12$
Division facts relating to the multiplication tables up to $12 \times 12$
Multiplication of decimals relating to the times tables up to $12 \times 12$
Division of decimals relating to the times tables up to $12 \times 12$
Multiplication and division of multiples of 10 and 100 relating to
  times tables up to $12 \times 12$
Use of $+$, $-$, $\times$ and $\div$ signs
Squares and square roots
Finding fractions of numbers using multiplication and division
Perimeters and areas of shapes
Find the mean average
Units of measurement for length, mass, capacity, time

# Section 1  Test 1

## A

| | | ANSWER |
|---|---|---|
| 1 | 5p + 5p + 5p + 5p | **20p** |
| 2 | 3 × 10 | **30** |
| 3 | Double 7 is | **14** |
| 4 | 3 + 3 + 3 + 3 + 3 | **15** |
| 5 | 2 × 9 kg | **18** kg |
| 6 | 50 ÷ 5 | **10** |
| 7 | Half of 16 cm is | **8** cm |
| 8 | 4 × [ ] = 12 | **3** |
| 9 | 0 ÷ 10 | **0** |
| 10 | 5 twos = [ ] fives | **2** |

## B

| | | ANSWER |
|---|---|---|
| 1 | Multiply 5 by 5. | **25** |
| 2 | How many 10p coins are worth 90p? | **9** |
| 3 | Seven times the value of a coin is 35p. What is the value of the coin? | **5p** |
| 4 | How many millimetres are there in 4 cm? | **40** |
| 5 | Divide 12 by 2. | **6** |
| 6 | What are nine groups of 4? | **36** |
| 7 | There are twenty-four quarters. How many whole ones is that? | **6** |
| 8 | How many threes are there in twenty-one? | **7** |
| 9 | Which number, other than 1, 2, 8 and 16, divides exactly into 16? | **4** |
| 10 | How much greater is (5 × 6) than (4 × 7)? | **2** |

## C

| | | ANSWER |
|---|---|---|
| 1 | Lucy bought these books. How much did they cost?  | £2? |
| 2 | Find the difference between $\frac{1}{5}$ of 10 and 5 times 10. | 4? |
| 3 | One fifth of a number is 8. What is the number? | 4? |
| 4 | Five biscuits cost 45p. How much do three of the biscuits cost? | 27 |
| 5 | Three sweets have a mass of 9 g. How many sweets have a mass of 24 g? | 8 |
| 6 | What is the perimeter of this regular hexagon?  | 18 cm |
| 7 | Six oranges are cut into quarters. How many children can each have three of the pieces? | 8 |
| 8 | A jogger travelled at the speed of 10 km/h for 30 minutes. How many kilometres did she travel? | 5 |
| 9 | The radius of the circle is 9 cm. What is the length of the diagonal of the square?  | 18 cm |
| 10 | A car uses a litre of petrol to travel 4 km. How many litres will it use to travel 32 kilometres? | 8 |

In question 6: 3 cm

4

# Section 1  Test 2

## A

| | | ANSWER |
|---|---|---|
| 1 | [ ] × 4 = 24 | 6 |
| 2 | 7 + 7 + 7 = | 21 |
| 3 | 4 × 5 = | 20 |
| 4 | Half of 14 km is | 7 km |
| 5 | 40 cm ÷ 5 = | 8 cm |
| 6 | $\frac{1}{3}$ of 24 kg is | 8 kg |
| 7 | Double 9 is | 18 |
| 8 | 2p + 2p + 2p + 2p+ 2p + 2p = | 12p |
| 9 | 36 ÷ 4 = | 9 |
| 10 | 10 twos = [ ] fives | 4 |

## B

| | | ANSWER |
|---|---|---|
| 1 | How many 5p coins are equal in value to 45p? | 9 |
| 2 | What is one fifth of 30? | 6 |
| 3 | 8 plus 8 plus 8 plus 8 is | 32 |
| 4 | How much greater is (2 × 10) than (3 × 4)? | 8 |
| 5 | What is the product of 5 and 7? | 35 |
| 6 | Multiply (3 × 3) by 3. | 27 |
| 7 | How many fives are there in twenty-five? | 5 |
| 8 | 3 times [ ] = 18 | 6 |
| 9 | Share £28 equally between 4 boys. How much each? | £7 |
| 10 | How many times smaller is 4 than 40? | 10 |

## C

| | | ANSWER |
|---|---|---|
| 1 | Four cards cost £12. How much will 5 cards cost?  | £15 |
| 2 | Write the missing number. 4 × [ ] = 2 × 8 | 4 |
| 3 | What is the smallest number which can be divided by both 4 and 5 without a remainder? | 20 |
| 4 | A bar of chocolate has 36 chunks. Saba eats $\frac{1}{4}$ of the bar. How many chunks does she eat? 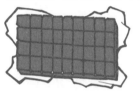 | 9 |
| 5 | Jack saves £10 a week. How long will it take him to save £90? | 9 weeks |
| 6 | A square has sides of 10 cm. What is its area? | 100 cm² |
| 7 | Which of these numbers can be divided by both 3 and 5 without a remainder? [9, 10, 12, 15, 18, 20, 25] | 15 |
| 8 | Jan gave 3 friends 9 sweets each and she had 5 sweets left. How many did she have to start with? | 32 |
| 9 | How long will it take to travel a distance of 40 km travelling at 5 km/h? | 8 h |
| 10 | How many pizzas can be bought for £45 if a box of 4 pizzas cost £5? | 36 |

5

# Section 1 Test 3

## A
| | | ANSWER |
|---|---|---|
| 1 | 10p + 10p + 10p + 10p = | 40p |
| 2 | $7 \times 0 =$ | 0 |
| 3 | $3 \times 9 = 9 + 9 +$ [ ] | 9 |
| 4 | 4 + 4 + 4 + 4 + 4 = | 20 |
| 5 | 6 m $\times$ 2 = 4 m + 4 m + [ ] | 4 m |
| 6 | 21 ÷ 3 | 7 |
| 7 | Half of 18 cm is | 9 cm |
| 8 | $4 \times$ [ ] = 28 | 7 |
| 9 | [ ] – 5 – 5 – 5 = 0 | 15 |
| 10 | $\frac{1}{5}$ of 30 kg is | 6 kg |

## B
| | | ANSWER |
|---|---|---|
| 1 | How many millimetres are there in 9 cm? | 90 |
| 2 | Divide 18 by 3. | 6 |
| 3 | What are eight groups of 4? | 32 |
| 4 | 9 kg plus 9 kg plus 9 kg is | 27 kg |
| 5 | How much greater is $(5 \times 5)$ than $(1 \times 10)$? | 15 |
| 6 | What is the product of 6 and 4? | 24 |
| 7 | Multiply $(2 \times 4)$ by 3. | 24 |
| 8 | 3 times 3 times 3 is | 27 |
| 9 | Find the difference between $\frac{1}{4}$ of 16 and $\frac{1}{2}$ of 20. | 6 |
| 10 | How many times larger is 45 km than 5 km? | 9 |

## C
| | | ANSWE |
|---|---|---|
| 1 | Jim has a five pound note. Pete has twice as much. Find the total of their money. | £15 |
| 2 | • stands for a missing sign, +, –, $\times$ or ÷. $8 \times 0 = 4 • 4$ What is the correct sign? | – |
| 3 | How many 5-litre cans can be filled from 40 litres of oil? | 8 |
| 4 | Divide the total of 29 and 6 by 5. | 7 |
| 5 | Find one quarter of the product of 8 and 3. | 6 |
| 6 | What is the perimeter of this regular pentagon? 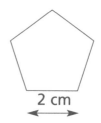 2 cm | 10 cm |
| 7 | Megan has 8p, Lauren has 7p, Dan has 9p and Alice 12p. If all their money is shared equally, how much will they each have? | 9p |
| 8 | A CD costs £4. How much change from £30 would you get if you bought 7 CDs? | £2 |
| 9 | Find the difference between $\frac{1}{3}$ of 18 and 3 times 6. | 12 |
| 10 | Which of these numbers will divide into 32 without a remainder? [6, 5, 4, 3] | 4 |

# Section 1  Test 4

## A

| | | ANSWER |
|---|---|---|
| 1 | $6 \times 10 =$ | 60 |
| 2 | Double 9 is | 18 |
| 3 | $5 \times [\ ] = 25$ | 5 |
| 4 | 2p + 2p + 2p + 2p + 2p + 2p | 12p |
| 5 | $3\overline{)24}$ | 8 |
| 6 | $4 \times 7 \times 0 =$ | 0 |
| 7 | $20 \text{ kg} \div 5 =$ | 4 kg |
| 8 | One quarter of 16 cm is | 4 cm |
| 9 | 10 twos = [ ] tens | 2 |
| 10 | $14 \div 2 =$ | 7 |

## B

| | | ANSWER |
|---|---|---|
| 1 | What is one third of 21m? | 7 m |
| 2 | Share £25 between 5 people. | £5 |
| 3 | How many threes are there in fifteen? | 5 |
| 4 | 4 times [ ] = 36 | 9 |
| 5 | How many 5p coins are worth 30p? | 6 |
| 6 | 7 plus 7 plus 7 plus 7 plus 7 is | 35 |
| 7 | What is the product of 3 and 6? | 18 |
| 8 | How many times smaller is 4 than 32? | 8 |
| 9 | How much greater is $(3 \times 10)$ than $(6 \times 4)$? | 6 |
| 10 | Multiply $(3 \times 3)$ by 5. | 45 |

## C

| | | ANSWER |
|---|---|---|
| 1 | Three consecutive numbers, when multiplied together, give 60. What are the numbers? | 3  4  5 |
| 2 | Five biscuits cost 40p. How much for 2 biscuits? | 16p |
| 3 | Find the difference between $\frac{1}{4}$ of 20 and 4 times 20. | 75 |
| 4 | One fifth of a number is 10. What is the number? | 50 |
| 5 | Four sweets have a mass of 12 g. How many sweets have a mass of 27 g? | 9 |
| 6 | What is the area of this rectangle? | 40 cm² |

8 cm

5 cm

| | | ANSWER |
|---|---|---|
| 7 | A truck uses a litre of petrol to travel 3 km. How many litres will it use to travel 21 kilometres? | 7 |
| 8 | Jo buys 4 kilograms of potatoes at £2 per kilogram. How much change from £10 does she get? | £2 |
| 9 | The mass of a parcel is 8 kg. How many times heavier is this parcel than a package weighing $\frac{1}{4}$ kg? | 32 |
| 10 | Three oranges are cut into quarters. How many children can each have two of the pieces? | 6 |

7

# Section 1   Test 5

## A

| | | ANSWER |
|---|---|---|
| 1 | £4 + £4 + £4 + £4 = | £16 |
| 2 | $3 \times 6 = 9 \times [\ ]$ | 2 |
| 3 | 8 + 8 + 8 = | 24 |
| 4 | $7 \times [\ ] = 7$ | 1 |
| 5 | $0 \times 9$ | 0 |
| 6 | $28 \div 4$ | 7 |
| 7 | Double 6 cm is | 12 cm |
| 8 | $4 \times [\ ] = 24$ | 6 |
| 9 | $45 - 5 - 5 = [\ ] \times 5$ | 7 |
| 10 | $\frac{1}{10}$ of 70 kg is | 7 kg |

## B

| | | ANSWER |
|---|---|---|
| 1 | Twice 8 = 4 times [\ ] | 4 |
| 2 | How many 5p coins are worth 40p? | 8 |
| 3 | Nine times the value of a coin is 45p. What is the value of the coin? | 5p |
| 4 | How many millimetres are there in 8 cm? | 80 |
| 5 | Divide 25 by 5. | 5 |
| 6 | What is the product of 8 and 4? | 32 |
| 7 | There are thirty-six quarters. How many whole ones is that? | 9 |
| 8 | How many threes are there in twenty-seven? | 9 |
| 9 | Which number, other than 1, 7 and 21, divides exactly into 21? | 3 |
| 10 | How much greater is $(4 \times 5)$ than $(3 \times 4)$? | 8 |

## C

| | | ANSWER |
|---|---|---|
| 1 | A square has sides of 3 cm. What is its area? | 9 cm |
| 2 | What is the smallest number which can be divided by both 4 and 6 without a remainder? | 1 |
| 3 | A packet contains 32 cookies. Ben eats $\frac{1}{4}$ of the packet. How many cookies does he eat?  | 8 |
| 4 | Clive saves £10 a month. How long will it take him to save enough to buy 6 CDs each costing £5? | 3 month |
| 5 | It takes an author 1 hour to write 4 pages. How long will it take her to write 24 pages? | 6 |
| 6 | Write the missing number. $4 \times [\ ] = 5 \times 8$ | 1 |
| 7 | Tom gave 4 friends 10 stickers each and he had 3 stickers left. How many did he have to start with? | 4 |
| 8 | How many pork pies can be bought for £15 if a packet of 4 pies cost £3? | 20 |
| 9 | 2 books cost £14. How much will 5 books cost?  | £35 |
| 10 | Thirty-six litres of oil fill 4 identical cans. How much does each can hold? | 9 |

# Section 1    Test 6

## A

| | | ANSWER |
|---|---|---|
| 1 | $\frac{1}{5}$ of 20 kg is | **4** kg |
| 2 | £3.00 + £3.00 + £3.00 = | **£9** |
| 3 | 3 × [ ] = 21 | **7** |
| 4 | 6 × 4 = 3 × [ ] | **8** |
| 5 | 36 ÷ 6 = | **6** |
| 6 | 1 × 1 = | **1** |
| 7 | (2 × 2) × (2 × 2) = | **16** |
| 8 | 7 × 4 = | **28** |
| 9 | $\frac{1}{2}$ of 18 mm is | **9** mm |
| 10 | [ ] ÷ 5 = 0 | **0** |

## B

| | | ANSWER |
|---|---|---|
| 1 | What is the product of 3 and 4? | **12** |
| 2 | How many groups of 3 are there in 18? | **6** |
| 3 | 3 times 3 times 5 is | **45** |
| 4 | What is the total mass of 5 sets of 5 kg? | **25** kg |
| 5 | What must 4 m be multiplied by to give 32 m? | **8** |
| 6 | How many times larger is 16 km than 4 km? | **4** |
| 7 | How much greater is (5 × 9) than (3 × 5)? | **30** |
| 8 | Multiply (2 × 3) by 5. | **30** |
| 9 | Divide £40 by 5. | **£8** |
| 10 | What is 7 lots of 10 subtract 4 lots of 5? | **50** |

## C

| | | ANSWER |
|---|---|---|
| 1 | This line is 5 cm long. Another is 7 times longer. What is its length? _____ | **35** cm |
| 2 | Forty-five chairs are arranged in rows of 5. How many rows? | **9** |
| 3 | • stands for a missing sign, +, −, × or ÷. 7 × 10 = (7 × 5) • 2  What is the correct sign? | **×** |
| 4 | What number, when multiplied by 4, will give a product of 40? | **10** |
| 5 | Divide the total of 9 and 7 by 4. | **4** |
| 6 | What is the area of this rectangle? | **24** cm² |

6 cm

4 cm

| | | |
|---|---|---|
| 7 | Which of these numbers will divide into 28 without a remainder? [6, 5, 4, 3] | **4** |
| 8 | Ella has 6p, Katie has 8p, Dean has 12p and David 10p. If all their money is shared equally, how much will they each have? | **9p** |
| 9 | A t-shirt costs £4 and a pair of shorts costs £6. How much will it cost in total to buy 5 t-shirts and 3 pairs of shorts? | **£38** |
| 10 | What is the perimeter of an equilateral triangle with sides of 6 cm? | **18** cm |

# Section 1    Test 7

## A                                    ANSWER

1  £6 + £6 + £6 + £6 =        £24

2  7 × 7 =                         49

3  Three eights are             24

4  9 + 9 + 9 + 9 + 9 + 9 =    54

5  [ ] ÷ 9 = 9                    81

6  32 ÷ 4 =                       8

7  $\frac{1}{8}$ of 16 cm is       2 cm

8  7 × [ ] = 14                   2

9  28 kg ÷ 4                     7 kg

10  (4 × 2) × (3 × 2) =          48

## B                                    ANSWER

1  Share £36 equally among
   6 boys. How much each?      £6

2  Find the remainder when 29
   is divided by 3.                2

3  What must 5 m be
   multiplied by to give 45 m?    9

4  How many millimetres are
   there in 10 cm?              100

5  Divide 72 by 9.                8

6  What is the product of 6 and 3?  18

7  How many times smaller
   is 4 than 36?                  9

8  What are eight groups of 5?   40

9  7 kg multiplied by 9 is      63 kg

10  $\frac{1}{8}$ of 32 is          4

## C                                    ANSWE

1  A boy earns £6 every day
   doing a paper round.
   How much does he earn
   in one week?                 £4.

2  What is the difference
   between $\frac{1}{7}$ of 21 and $\frac{1}{7}$ of 35?   2

3  Six identical terraced houses
   are in a row. The row is 24 m
   wide. What is the width of
   each house?                  4 r

4  A jogger travelled at
   the speed of 8 km/h for
   15 minutes. How far did
   she run?                     2 kr

5  The radius of the circle
   is 8 cm. What is the length
   of the diagonal of the square?

                                 16 cr

6  Nine biscuits cost 18p.
   How much do five of the
   biscuits cost?               10

7  Eight sweets have a mass
   of 56 g. How many sweets
   have a mass of 70g?          10

8  Nine apples are cut into
   quarters. Six children share
   the pieces. How many do
   they each get?               6

9  A car uses a litre of petrol
   to travel 8 km. How many
   litres will it use to travel
   56 kilometres?               7

10  One eighth of a number
   is 10. What is the number?   80

# Section 1 Test 8

## A

| | | ANSWER |
|---|---|---|
| 1 | $8 \times 8 =$ | 64 |
| 2 | [ ] $\div 8 = 0$ | 0 |
| 3 | $\frac{1}{9}$ of £72 is | £8 |
| 4 | $36 \div 9 = 32 \div$ [ ] | 8 |
| 5 | $6 \times 9$ km = | 54 km |
| 6 | $(8 \times 3) \div 4 =$ | 6 |
| 7 | One third of 18 cm is | 6 cm |
| 8 | $7 \times$ [ ] $= 56$ | 8 |
| 9 | [ ] $- 9 - 9 - 9 = 0$ | 27 |
| 10 | $2 \times 3 \times 4 =$ | 24 |

## B

| | | ANSWER |
|---|---|---|
| 1 | How many 5p coins are equal in value to 40p? | 8 |
| 2 | What is one sixth of 54? | 9 |
| 3 | What is 6 times 5, divided by 10? | 3 |
| 4 | How much greater is $(5 \times 5)$ than $(4 \times 4)$? | 9 |
| 5 | What is the product of 0 and 9? | 0 |
| 6 | Multiply $(2 \times 3)$ by 7. | 42 |
| 7 | Twice $6 = 4$ times [ ] | 3 |
| 8 | Divide 48 by 8. | 6 |
| 9 | There are thirty-two quarters. How many whole ones is that? | 8 |
| 10 | What is the remainder when 50 is divided by 7? | 1 |

## C

| | | ANSWER |
|---|---|---|
| 1 | A petrol tank, which holds 24 litres, is one quarter full. How many more litres will it take to fill it? | 18 |
| 2 | Jan gave 4 friends 7 sweets each and she had 5 sweets left. How many did she have to start with? | 33 |
| 3 | Three biscuits cost 27p. How much do seven of the biscuits cost? | 63p |
| 4 | A square has sides of 9 cm. What is the area of the square? | 81 cm² |

5  Six of these circular discs are placed side by side touching in a line. What is their total length?

| | | |
|---|---|---|
| | 3 cm   3 cm   3 cm | 18 cm |

| | | ANSWER |
|---|---|---|
| 6 | Which of these numbers can be divided by both 6 and 7 without a remainder? [12, 14, 18, 21, 24, 35, 42] | 42 |
| 7 | A car uses a litre of petrol to travel 8 km. How many litres will it use to travel 64 kilometres? | 8 |
| 8 | Find the difference between $\frac{1}{8}$ of 56 and $\frac{1}{8}$ of 24. | 4 |
| 9 | Harry has a ten pound note. William has five times as much as that. Find the total of their money. | £60 |
| 10 | • stands for a missing sign, $+, -, \times$ or $\div$. $0 \times 4 = 8 \cdot 8$ What is the correct sign? | − |

# Section 1  Test 9

## A

| | | ANSWER |
|---|---|---|
| 1 | $6\overline{)48}$ | 8 |
| 2 | $3 \times 7 =$ | 21 |
| 3 | 9 fives are | 45 |
| 4 | $4 \times [\ ] = £32$ | £8 |
| 5 | $9 \times 6 \times 2 \times 0 =$ | 0 |
| 6 | $7p + 7p + 7p + 7p + 7p + 7p =$ | 42p |
| 7 | $72 \text{ kg} \div 8 =$ | 9 kg |
| 8 | One quarter of 24 cm is | 6 cm |
| 9 | $14 \div 2 =$ | 7 |
| 10 | $30 \div 7 = [\ ] \text{ r } [\ \ ]$ | 4 r 2 |

## B

| | | ANSWER |
|---|---|---|
| 1 | 6 plus 6 plus 6 plus 6 is | 24 |
| 2 | What is the product of 6 and 6? | 36 |
| 3 | What is one ninth of 36 m? | 4 m |
| 4 | Share £40 equally between 8 people. | £5 |
| 5 | How many eights are there in twenty-four? | 3 |
| 6 | 9 times [ ] = 36 | 4 |
| 7 | How many times heavier is 54 kg than 6 kg? | 9 |
| 8 | How much smaller is $(8 \times 10)$ than $(9 \times 9)$? | 1 |
| 9 | Multiply $(2 \times 4)$ by 7. | 56 |
| 10 | What number is equal to $(9 \times 7) + 7$? | 70 |

## C

| | | ANSWE |
|---|---|---|
| 1 | Three note books cost £4.50. What will be the cost of 9 notebooks? | £13.5 |
| 2 | One eighth of a number is 8. What is the number? | 64 |
| 3 | Write the missing number. $4 \times [\ ] = 5 \times 8$ | 10 |
| 4 | What is the smallest number which can be divided by both 7 and 8 without a remainder? | 56 |
| 5 | A bar of chocolate has 36 chunks. Josh eats $\frac{1}{6}$ of the bar. How many chunks does he eat? | |

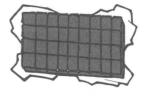

| | | 6 |
|---|---|---|
| 6 | What is the perimeter of an equilateral triangle with sides of 7 cm? | 21 cm |
| 7 | A cyclist travels at 16 km per hour. How far does he cycle in 15 minutes? | 4 km |
| 8 | Urvi has 8p, Fred has 7p and Dev has 12p. If all their money is shared equally, how much will they each have? | 9p |
| 9 | Nine kg cost 45p. Find the price per kg. | 5p |
| 10 | A square mosaic tile has an area of 7 cm². 7 tiles are used to make a shape, without gaps. What is the area of the shape? | 49 cm |

# Section 1    Test 10

## A

| | | ANSWER |
|---|---|---|
| 1 | $38 \div 5 = [\ \ ]\ r\ [\ \ ]$ | 7 r 3 |
| 2 | How many days in 4 weeks? | 28 |
| 3 | $9 + 9 + 9 + 9 + 9 =$ | 45 |
| 4 | $8 \times 6$ kg $=$ | 48 kg |
| 5 | $36 \div 4 =$ | 9 |
| 6 | $7\overline{)42}$ | 6 |
| 7 | $4 \times [\ \ ] = 16$ | 4 |
| 8 | $8 \times 8 =$ | 64 |
| 9 | $\frac{1}{8}$ of 24 cm | 3 cm |
| 10 | $(7 \times 1) \times 3 =$ | 21 |

## B

| | | ANSWER |
|---|---|---|
| 1 | Multiply 6 by 9. | 54 |
| 2 | How many 10p coins are worth 70p? | 7 |
| 3 | Divide 30 by 6. | 5 |
| 4 | What are eight groups of 7? | 56 |
| 5 | There are twenty quarters. How many whole ones is that? | 5 |
| 6 | How many centimetres is 60 mm? | 6 |
| 7 | Which number, other than 1, 2, 3, 9 and 18, divides exactly into 18? | 6 |
| 8 | How many sixes are there in twenty-four? | 4 |
| 9 | How much greater is $(8 \times 9)$ than $(10 \times 7)$? | 2 |
| 10 | What is one third of 27 kg? | 9 kg |

## C

| | | ANSWER |
|---|---|---|
| 1 | • stands for a missing sign, +, −, × or ÷. $0 \div 6 = 3 • 3$ What is the correct sign? | − |
| 2 | How many 8-litre cans can be filled from 32 litres of oil? | 4 |
| 3 | Sam has a five pound note. Sara has 8 times as much as that. Find the total of their money. | £45 |
| 4 | Divide the total of 43 and 6 by 7. | 7 |
| 5 | Which of these numbers will divide into 27 without a remainder? [6, 5, 4, 3] | 3 |
| 6 | The perimeter of a square is 12 cm. What is its area? | 9 cm² |
| 7 | A CD costs £6. How much change from £50 would you get if you bought 7 CDs? | £8 |
| 8 | What is one quarter of the product of 6 and 6? | 9 |
| 9 | What is the perimeter of this regular pentagon? 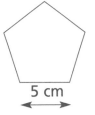 5 cm | 25 cm |
| 10 | Find the difference between $\frac{1}{5}$ of 35 and 3 times 5. | 8 |

# Section 1  Test 11

## A

| | | ANSWER |
|---|---|---|
| 1 | $3 \times 7$ kg = | **21 kg** |
| 2 | $(7 \div 1) \times (6 \times 0)$ = | **0** |
| 3 | $54 \div 6$ = | **9** |
| 4 | $6 \times [\ \ ] = 24$ | **4** |
| 5 | $(3 \times 2) \times [\ \ ] = 48$ | **8** |
| 6 | £8 + £8 + £8 + £8 = | **£32** |
| 7 | $64 \div 8$ = | **8** |
| 8 | $\frac{1}{9}$ of 63 m is | **7 m** |
| 9 | $[\ \ ] \div 9 = 9$ | **81** |
| 10 | $35 - 5 - 5 - 5 = [\ \ ] \times 5$ | **4** |

## B

| | | ANSWER |
|---|---|---|
| 1 | What is one sixth of 30 km? | **5 km** |
| 2 | Share £49 equally between 7 people. | **£7** |
| 3 | How many sevens are there in fifty-six? | **8** |
| 4 | What number is equal to 4 times 9? | **36** |
| 5 | What is the product of 7 and 6? | **42** |
| 6 | How many times smaller is 8 than 72? | **9** |
| 7 | How much greater is $(4 \times 10)$ than $(6 \times 6)$? | **4** |
| 8 | Multiply $(2 \times 3)$ by 9. | **54** |
| 9 | Share £28 between 7 boys. How much each? | **£4** |
| 10 | How many quarters in 5? | **20** |

## C

| | | ANSWE |
|---|---|---|
| 1 | When 48 is divided by a number the answer is 6. What is the number? | 8 |
| 2 | What is the total cost of 4 packets of chews and 3 packets of sweets?  | 37 |
| 3 | Trisha gave 3 friends 8 sweets each and she had 7 sweets left. How many did she have to start with? | 31 |
| 4 | One seventh of a number is 5. What is the number? | 35 |
| 5 | £18 is shared between Mo and Sash. Mo gets 5 times as much as Sash. How much does Mo get? | £15 |
| 6 | Eight sweets have a mass of 56 g. How many sweets have a mass of 21 g? | 3 |
| 7 | A car uses a litre of petrol to travel 9 km. How many litres will it use to travel 72 kilometres? | 8 |
| 8 | A car travelled at the speed of 36 km/h for 15 minutes. How many kilometres did it travel? | 9 |
| 9 | This line is 4 cm long. Another is 8 times longer. What is its length? ————————— | 32 cm |
| 10 | What is the difference between the number of days in 9 weeks and the number of minutes in one hour? | 3 |

# Section 1 Test 12

## A

| | | ANSWER |
|---|---|---|
| 1 | $\frac{1}{6}$ of 42 kg is | 7 kg |
| 2 | $1 \times 1 \times 1 \times 1 =$ | 1 |
| 3 | $9 \times [ \ ] = 54$ | 6 |
| 4 | £9.00 + £9.00 + £9.00 = | £27 |
| 5 | $6 \div 6 = 3 \div [ \ ]$ | 3 |
| 6 | $49 \div 6 = [ \ ]$ r $[ \ ]$ | 8 r 1 |
| 7 | $6 \times 9 \times 4 \times 0 =$ | 0 |
| 8 | $(3 \times 3) \times 7 =$ | 63 |
| 9 | $\frac{1}{8}$ of 64 mm is | 8 mm |
| 10 | $[ \ ] \div 10 = 5$ | 50 |

## B

| | | ANSWER |
|---|---|---|
| 1 | Twice 9 = 3 times [ ] | 6 |
| 2 | Five times the value of a coin is 25p. What is the value of the coin? | 5p |
| 3 | How many times less than 72 is 9? | 8 |
| 4 | Divide 32 by 4. | 8 |
| 5 | What is the product of 8 and 7? | 56 |
| 6 | Share the amount of money equal to nine 5p coins equally between 5 girls. How much each? | 9p |
| 7 | There are thirty-six quarters. How many whole ones is that? | 9 |
| 8 | Which number, other than 1, 2, 8 and 16, divides exactly into 16? | 4 |
| 9 | By how much is $\frac{1}{7}$ of 49 greater than $\frac{1}{4}$ of 12? | 4 |
| 10 | How many times heavier is 42 kg than 7 kg? | 6 |

## C

| | | ANSWER |
|---|---|---|
| 1 | Thirty-six chairs are arranged in rows of 6. How many rows? | 6 |
| 2 | • stands for a missing sign, +, −, × or ÷. $7 \times 4 = (6 \times 5) • 2$ What is the correct sign? | − |
| 3 | A t-shirt costs £3 and a pair of shorts costs £7. How much will it cost in total to buy 4 t-shirts and 3 pairs of shorts? | £33 |
| 4 | What number, when multiplied by 5, will give a product of 40? | 8 |
| 5 | Divide the total of 18 and 6 by 4. | 6 |
| 6 | Matt has 20p, Kieran has 5p, Flynn has 10p and Mia has 1p. If all their money is shared equally, how much will they each have? | 9p |
| 7 | What is the area of this rectangle? | 28 cm² |

7 cm

4 cm

| | | ANSWER |
|---|---|---|
| 8 | Which of these numbers will divide into 81 without a remainder? [6, 7, 8, 9] | 9 |
| 9 | What is the perimeter of a regular hexagon with sides of 5 cm? | 30 cm |
| 10 | One seventh of a number is 8. What is the number? | 56 |

# Progress Test 1

Write the numbers 1 to 20 down the side of a sheet of paper.
Write alongside these numbers the **answers only** to the following questions.
Work as quickly as you can.
Time allowed – **10 minutes.**

| 1 | $4 \times 6 =$ | 24 |
|---|---|---|
| 2 | Share £40 equally between 8 people. | £5 |
| 3 | What is the product of 3 and 7? | 21 |
| 4 | What is one fifth of 30 km? | 6 km |
| 5 | $54 \div 6 =$ | 9 |
| 6 | When 32 is divided by a number the answer is 4. What is the number? | 8 |
| 7 | There are twenty-eight quarters. How many whole ones is that? | 7 |
| 8 | Which of these numbers can be divided by both 6 and 8 without a remainder? [18, 30, 36, 42, 48, 56] | 48 |
| 9 | The mass of a parcel is 4 kg. How many times heavier is this parcel than a package weighing $\frac{1}{4}$ kg? | 16 |
| 10 | This line is 5 cm long. Another is 9 times longer. What is its length? _____ | 45 cm |
| 11 | How many 7-litre cans can be filled from 35 litres of oil? | 5 |
| 12 | What is the remainder when 50 is divided by 7? | 1 |
| 13 | What is the perimeter of this regular hexagon? 7 cm | 42 cm |
| 14 | What is the smallest number which can be divided by both 4 and 9 without a remainder? | 36 |
| 15 | Three biscuits cost 27p. How much do eight of the biscuits cost? | 72p |
| 16 | A car uses a litre of petrol to travel 9 km. How many litres will it use to travel 63 kilometres? | 7 |
| 17 | A t-shirt costs £6 and a pair of shorts costs £7. How much will it cost in total to buy 6 t-shirts and 2 pairs of shorts? | £50 |
| 18 | The perimeter of a square is 36 cm. What is its area? | 81 cm² |
| 19 | A bar of chocolate has 24 chunks. Edgar eats $\frac{1}{3}$ of the bar. How many chunks does he eat? | 8 |
| 20 | Subtract the number of days in 8 weeks from 100. | 44 |

ou will work through Progress Test 1 at **four** different times. When you first work the test
   a) colour the first column to show the number of examples correct out of 20
   b) enter the date.
ach time you work the test, enter the result and the date in the marked columns.

|      | 1st | 2nd | 3rd | 4th |
|------|-----|-----|-----|-----|
| 20   |     |     |     |     |
| 19   |     |     |     |     |
| 18   |     |     |     |     |
| 17   |     |     |     |     |
| 16   |     |     |     |     |
| 15   |     |     |     |     |
| 14   |     |     |     |     |
| 13   |     |     |     |     |
| 12   |     |     |     |     |
| 11   |     |     |     |     |
| 10   |     |     |     |     |
| 9    |     |     |     |     |
| 8    |     |     |     |     |
| 7    |     |     |     |     |
| 6    |     |     |     |     |
| 5    |     |     |     |     |
| 4    |     |     |     |     |
| 3    |     |     |     |     |
| 2    |     |     |     |     |
| 1    |     |     |     |     |
| 0    |     |     |     |     |
| date |     |     |     |     |

# Section 2   Test 1

## A

| | | ANSWER |
|---|---|---|
| 1 | $30 \times 8 =$ | 240 |
| 2 | 6 squared is | 36 |
| 3 | $40 + 40 + 40 + 40 =$ | 160 |
| 4 | $\frac{2}{3}$ of 9 kg is | 6 kg |
| 5 | $630 \div 9 =$ | 70 |
| 6 | One quarter of 32 cm is | 8 cm |
| 7 | $6 \times [\ ] = 30$ | 5 |
| 8 | $52 \div 10 = [\ ]$ r $[\ ]$ | 5 r 2 |
| 9 | $7 \times 8 =$ | 56 |
| 10 | 4 tens = [ ] fives | 8 |

## B

| | | ANSWER |
|---|---|---|
| 1 | What is 9 squared? | 81 |
| 2 | There are twenty-one thirds. How many whole ones is that? | 7 |
| 3 | Find three quarters of 36. | 27 |
| 4 | How many millimetres are there in 30 cm? | 300 |
| 5 | Divide 280 by 4. | 70 |
| 6 | What are seven groups of 6? | 42 |
| 7 | How many eights are there in forty-eight? | 6 |
| 8 | What is the remainder when 57 is divided by 6? | 3 |
| 9 | How much smaller is $(5 \times 7)$ than $(4 \times 9)$? | 1 |
| 10 | Share £720 between 9 boys. How much each? | £80 |

## C

| | | ANSWER |
|---|---|---|
| 1 | How many weeks is equal to 49 days? | 7 |
| 2 | What is the difference between $\frac{1}{3}$ of 9 and 3 times 9? | 24 |
| 3 | One eighth of a number is 8. What is the number? | 64 |
| 4 | Six biscuits cost 18p. How much do four of the biscuits cost? | 12p |
| 5 | A jogger travelled at the speed of 10 km/h for 6 minutes. How many kilometres did she travel? | 1 |
| 6 | A 56 cm plank of wood is cut into eight pieces of equal length. What is the length of one of these pieces? | 7 cm |
| 7 | Find one quarter of the product of 5 and 8. | 10 |
| 8 | How many half oranges can be cut from seven whole oranges? | 14 |
| 9 | What is the perimeter of this regular octagon? | 24 cm |

3 cm

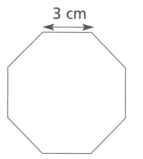

| | | |
|---|---|---|
| 10 | There are seven times as many adults as children on a bus. There are 3 children. How many people on the bus? | 24 |

# Section 2　Test 2

## A

| | | ANSWER |
|---|---|---|
| 1 | $\frac{1}{4}$ of 360° is | 90° |
| 2 | [ ] × 5 = 15 | 3 |
| 3 | 9 + 9 + 9 + 9 + 9 + 9 + 9 = | 63 |
| 4 | 40 × 60 = | 2400 |
| 5 | One fifth of 250 km is | 50 km |
| 6 | 72 cm ÷ 9 = | 8 cm |
| 7 | Six sixes are | 36 |
| 8 | $4^2$ = | 16 |
| 9 | 56 ÷ [ ] = 2 × 4 | 7 |
| 10 | 55 ÷ 6 = [ ] r [ ] | 9 r 1 |

## B

| | | ANSWER |
|---|---|---|
| 1 | What is the remainder when 33 is divided by 8? | 1 |
| 2 | How many 5p coins are equal in value to 150p? | 30 |
| 3 | What is the product of 30 and 7? | 210 |
| 4 | 7 plus 7 plus 7 plus 7 plus 7 plus 7 is | 42 |
| 5 | What is 60 g multiplied by 8? | 480 g |
| 6 | How many sevens are there in thirty-five? | 5 |
| 7 | Multiply (30 × 30) by 30. | 27 000 |
| 8 | How much greater is 8 squared than 7 squared? | 15 |
| 9 | 6 times [ ] = 48 | 8 |
| 10 | Share £81 equally between 9 girls. How much each? | £9 |

## C

| | | ANSWER |
|---|---|---|
| 1 | Deepa is 4 times younger than her mother. Deepa is 7 years old. How old will her mother be in 2 years' time? | 30 |
| 2 | Write the missing number. 9 × 9 = 10 × 10 − [ ] | 19 |
| 3 | What is the smallest number which can be divided by both 8 and 6 without a remainder? | 24 |
| 4 | Chris earns £5 a day. How many weeks will it take him to save £70? | 2 |
| 5 | The distance from Matby to Haw is one third of the distance from Haw to Skern. How far it is from Matby to Skern via Haw? | 32 km |

| | | ANSWER |
|---|---|---|
| 6 | A rectangle is 9 cm long and 5 cm wide. What is its area? | 45 cm² |
| 7 | A map shows lengths 30 times smaller than in real life. How long, in real life, is a length that is 9 cm on the map? | 270 cm |
| 8 | How long will it take to travel a distance of 180 km travelling at 60 km/h? | 3 h |
| 9 | How many stickers can be bought for 63p if a box of 4 stickers cost 7p? | 36 |
| 10 | Find one ninth of the product of 6 and 30. | 20 |

# Section 2  Test 3

## A

| | | ANSWER |
|---|---|---|
| 1 | 61 ÷ 9 = [ ] r [ ] | 6 r 7 |
| 2 | (8 × 40) + (6 × 10) = | 380 |
| 3 | 50p × 7 = £[ ] | 3.50 |
| 4 | 600 ml × 5 = | 3000 ml |
| 5 | $\frac{1}{6}$ of 360° is | 60° |
| 6 | 64 ÷ 8 = 70 − [ ] | 62 |
| 7 | 4 × [ ] = 28 | 7 |
| 8 | [ ] − 7 − 7 − 7 = 0 | 21 |
| 9 | 480 minutes = [ ] hours | 8 |
| 10 | $\frac{2}{7}$ of 49 kg is | 14 kg |

## B

| | | ANSWER |
|---|---|---|
| 1 | How many minutes in 4 hours? | 240 |
| 2 | Divide 18 by 3 and then multiply by 9. | 54 |
| 3 | Multiply the sum of 6 and 2 by 4. | 32 |
| 4 | 8 kg plus 8 kg plus 8 kg is | 24 kg |
| 5 | How much greater is (6 × 7) than (4 × 9)? | 6 |
| 6 | What is the product of 9 and 9? | 81 |
| 7 | Find the square of (3 × 2). | 36 |
| 8 | 20 times 3 times 10 is | 600 |
| 9 | How much greater is 4 squared than 3 squared? | 7 |
| 10 | How many times larger is 63 km than 7 km? | 9 |

## C

| | | ANSWE |
|---|---|---|
| 1 | Paul has 80p. Meg has nine times as much as that. Find the total of their money. | £8 |
| 2 | Forty-five pencils were put into packets of 5. How many packets were there altogether? | 9 |
| 3 | • stands for a missing sign, +, −, × or ÷. 30 × 40 = 120 • 10 What is the correct sign? | x |
| 4 | How many 500-millilitre cups can be filled from 9 litres of water? | 18 |
| 5 | Find the square of 7 and add 7. Then divide the total by 8. | 7 |
| 6 | The perimeter of this regular hexagon is 240 mm.<br><br>What is the length of one of its sides? | |

|  |  | 40 mm |
|---|---|---|

| | | |
|---|---|---|
| 7 | A CD costs £4. How much change from £30 would you get if you bought 7 CDs? | £2 |
| 8 | Eight parcels each have a mass of 900 g. How much less than $7\frac{1}{2}$ kg is their total mass? | 300 g |
| 9 | Find the difference between $\frac{3}{4}$ of 16 and $\frac{2}{5}$ of 20. | 4 |
| 10 | Which of these numbers is a multiple of 70? [45, 620, 49, 420, 100] | 420 |

20

# Section 2   Test 4

## A

| | | ANSWER |
|---|---|---|
| 1 | $7\overline{)56}$ | 8 |
| 2 | 400 g × 8 = | 3200 g |
| 3 | 5 squared is | 25 |
| 4 | 300 minutes = [   ] hours | 5 |
| 5 | 40 ÷ 9 = [   ] r [   ] | 4 r 4 |
| 6 | [ ] ÷ 7 = 7 | 49 |
| 7 | 40 × 50 × 0 × 20 = | 0 |
| 8 | 450 ÷ 5 = | 90 |
| 9 | $\frac{3}{10}$ of 90 cm is | 27 cm |
| 10 | £1.50 ÷ 3 = [   ] p | 50 |

## B

| | | ANSWER |
|---|---|---|
| 1 | What is one third of 27 m? | 9 m |
| 2 | What will be the cost of 7 pencils at 60p each? | £4.20 |
| 3 | What is the product of 60 and 9? | 540 |
| 4 | How many minutes in 6 hours? | 360 |
| 5 | How many threes are there in fifteen? | 5 |
| 6 | 4 times [   ] = 36 | 9 |
| 7 | Divide 65 by 9. | 7 r 2 |
| 8 | What is $\frac{3}{8}$ of 32? | 12 |
| 9 | How much greater is 10 squared than 9 squared? | 19 |
| 10 | Multiply (40 × 2) by 30. | 2400 |

## C

| | | ANSWER |
|---|---|---|
| 1 | Three consecutive numbers, when multiplied together, give 210. What are the numbers? | 5   6   7 |
| 2 | A strip half a metre long is cut into 7-centimetre lengths. How many centimetres remain? | 1 |
| 3 | Find the cost of 5 badges if 6 badges cost 42p. | 35p |
| 4 | Six pieces of wire each measure 8 cm. Find the total length of the pieces in millimetres. | 480 mm |
| 5 | In a game Hannah scored 40 times more points than Amy. Hannah scored 800 points. How many did Amy score? | 20 |
| 6 | Nine sweets have a mass of 72 g. How many sweets have a mass of 40 g? | 5 |
| 7 | A van uses a litre of petrol to travel 7 km. How many litres will it use to travel 280 kilometres? | 40 |
| 8 | Leah buys 4 kilograms of onions at 70p per kilogram. How much change does she get from £5? | £2.20 |
| 9 | The mass of a parcel is 8 kg. How many times heavier is this parcel than a package weighing $\frac{1}{4}$ kg? | 32 |
| 10 | Some tiles are 7 cm wide. How many tiles can be placed side by side on this strip? | 40 |

280 cm

# Section 2  Test 5

## A

| | | ANSWER |
|---|---|---|
| 1 | $3^2 + 1 =$ | 10 |
| 2 | $80 \times 5 = 4 \times [\quad]$ | 100 |
| 3 | $90° + 90° + 90° =$ | 270° |
| 4 | $[\quad] \div 5 = 5$ | 25 |
| 5 | $(7 \times 30) + (4 \times 50) =$ | 410 |
| 6 | $320 \div 40 =$ | 8 |
| 7 | $\frac{4}{5}$ of 45 kg is | 36 kg |
| 8 | 180 minutes = [   ] hours | 3 |
| 9 | $60 \div 8 = [\quad] r [\quad]$ | 7 r 4 |
| 10 | $49 - 7 - 7 = [\quad] \times 5$ | 7 |

## B

| | | ANSWER |
|---|---|---|
| 1 | How many days in 7 weeks? | 49 |
| 2 | What is four squared divided by 2? | 8 |
| 3 | What is seven eighths of 16 m? | 14 m |
| 4 | Apples cost 9p each. How much will 7 cost? | 63p |
| 5 | How many times longer is 48 km than 8 km? | 6 |
| 6 | What is the product of 9 and 6? | 54 |
| 7 | How many whole ones are equal to 42 sixths? | 7 |
| 8 | How many sixes are there in thirty? | 5 |
| 9 | Multiply 2 squared by 3. | 12 |
| 10 | How much greater is $(4 \times 5)$ than $(3 \times 4)$? | 8 |

## C

| | | ANSWE |
|---|---|---|
| 1 | A square has sides of 10 cm. What is its area? | 100 cm |
| 2 | Three 60° angles are joined together to make one angle. How large is it? | 180 |
| 3 | Three in every 5 sweets in a bag are orange. Twenty-one sweets are orange. How many sweets are there altogether in the bag? | 3! |
| 4 | An author writes 4 pages in 3 hours. At this rate how long will it take him to write 24 pages? | 18 |
| 5 | Subtract the product of six and six from the product of ten and ten. | 6 |
| 6 | Write the missing number. $9 \times [\quad] = 60 + 12$ | 8 |
| 7 | How many pencils can be bought for £8.10 if a packet of 8 pencils cost 90p? | 72 |
| 8 | To $\frac{2}{3}$ of 24p, add $\frac{4}{5}$ of 30p. | 40 |
| 9 | The distance from Anby to Ugby is four fifths of the distance from Anby to Wells. How far it is from Anby to Wells via Ugby? | 35 km |
| 10 | 3600 ml of oil fill 6 identical containers. How much does each hold? | 600 m |

# Section 2 Test 6

## A

| | | ANSWER |
|---|---|---|
| 1 | $360° ÷ 4 =$ | 90° |
| 2 | $\frac{5}{6}$ of 42 kg is | 35 kg |
| 3 | £80 + £80 + £80 + £80 = | £320 |
| 4 | $3 × [\ ] = 2100$ | 700 |
| 5 | $(56 ÷ 7) × 3 =$ | 24 |
| 6 | $9 × 9 × 3 × 0 =$ | 0 |
| 7 | $\frac{7}{10}$ of 700 mm is | 490 mm |
| 8 | $400\ g × 4 =$ | 1600 g |
| 9 | $[\ ] ÷ 9 = 100$ | 900 |
| 10 | $3^2 × 2^2 =$ | 36 |

## B

| | | ANSWER |
|---|---|---|
| 1 | What is the product of 80 and 60? | 4800 |
| 2 | How many times longer is 720 km than 8 km? | 90 |
| 3 | How many groups of 30p are there in £2.70? | 9 |
| 4 | What is 40 times 5 times 90? | 18 000 |
| 5 | Find the total mass of 5 parcels of 600 g in kg. | 3 kg |
| 6 | Divide 4 squared by 8. | 2 |
| 7 | What must 6 m be multiplied by to give 540 m? | 90 |
| 8 | What is $(45 ÷ 9)$ minus $(28 ÷ 7)$? | 1 |
| 9 | Divide £640 by 8. | £80 |
| 10 | Find the difference between $7 × 8$ and $6 × 9$. | 2 |

## C

| | | ANSWER |
|---|---|---|
| 1 | Sixty-three children are grouped in teams of 9. How many teams? | 7 |
| 2 | What number, when multiplied by 9, will give a product that is half of 90? | 5 |
| 3 | A prize of £8100 is shared equally between 9 people. How much money will they each receive? | £900 |
| 4 | This line is 36 mm long. How many millimetres is a line that is $\frac{5}{9}$ of its length? _____ | 20 mm |
| 5 | Divide the square of 20 by 10. | 40 |
| 6 | What is the perimeter of this equilateral triangle? | 90 cm |

30 cm

| | | |
|---|---|---|
| 7 | Which of these numbers will divide into 42 without a remainder? [4, 6, 8, 9] | 6 |
| 8 | A small bag of sugar holds 400 g.  How many of these bags do you need to have 2.8 kg of sugar? | 7 |
| 9 | The angles in this diagram are equal. What is the size of angle $x$? | 45° |
| 10 | Nine pieces of ribbon of length 9 cm are cut from a metre length. How much ribbon is left? | 19 cm |

# Section 2  Test 7

## A

| | | ANSWER |
|---|---|---|
| 1 | $0.5 \times [\ ] = 4.5$ | 9 |
| 2 | $11 \times 7 =$ | 77 |
| 3 | $4^2 + 2^2 =$ | 20 |
| 4 | Three twelves are | 36 |
| 5 | $0.9 \times [\ ] = 5.4$ | 6 |
| 6 | $[\ ] \div 5 = 5$ | 25 |
| 7 | $22 \div 11 =$ | 2 |
| 8 | $\frac{3}{7}$ of 42 cm is | 18 cm |
| 9 | $8 \overline{)64}$ | 8 |
| 10 | $(5 \times 12) - (6 \times 10) =$ | 0 |

## B

| | | ANSWER |
|---|---|---|
| 1 | What are eight groups of 9? | 72 |
| 2 | What is the square root of 49? | 7 |
| 3 | Share £3.60 equally among 9 boys. How much each? | 40p |
| 4 | Find the remainder when 40 is divided by 6. | 4 |
| 5 | Divide 4.8 by 6. | 0.8 |
| 6 | What is the product of 0.7 and 4? | 2.8 |
| 7 | What is $\frac{7}{8}$ of 24? | 21 |
| 8 | How many times smaller is 3 than 33? | 11 |
| 9 | What is 0.3 kg multiplied by 9? | 2.7 kg |
| 10 | How many months are there in 6 years? | 72 |

## C

| | | ANSWER |
|---|---|---|
| 1 | Six pieces of ribbon are cut, each 0.4 m in length. What is their total length? | 2.4 m |
| 2 | Find the difference between $(0.4 \times 5)$ and $(1.2 \div 0.3)$. | 2 |
| 3 | A scale drawing shows lengths 9 times smaller than in real life. How long, in real life, is a length that is 0.9 cm on the drawing? | 8.1 cm |
| 4 | How long will it take to travel a distance of 63 km travelling at 9 km/h? | 7 h |
| 5 | What is the mean of these 4 numbers?  [11, 12, 5, 4 ] | 8 |
| 6 | A rectangle is 7 cm long and 0.8 cm wide. What is its area? | 5.6 cm |
| 7 | The square root of a number is 3 more than the square root of 4. What is the number? | 25 |
| 8 | If it costs £0.50 to travel 5 km, how much will it cost to travel 45 km at the same rate? | £4.50 |
| 9 | What is the perimeter of a regular decagon with sides of 0.06 m? | 0.6 m |
| 10 | How many grams more than 3 kg is the mass of the contents of 4 of these tins? | 200 g |

0.8Kg
NET MASS

# Section 2  Test 8

## A

| | | ANSWER |
|---|---|---|
| 1 | $(80 \times 30) \div 400 =$ | 6 |
| 2 | $11 \times 10 =$ | 110 |
| 3 | $[\quad] \div 12 = 2$ | 24 |
| 4 | $\frac{7}{9}$ of £54 is | £42 |
| 5 | $6 \times 8 = [\quad] \times 12$ | 4 |
| 6 | $[\ ] \times 8 = 5.6$ | 0.7 |
| 7 | $4 \times 0.7$ km $=$ | 2.8 km |
| 8 | The square of 7 cm is | 49 cm² |
| 9 | $40 \div 9 = [\quad]$ r $[\quad]$ | 4 r 4 |
| 10 | $2 \times 3 \times 2 \times 5 \times 2 =$ | 120 |

## B

| | | ANSWER |
|---|---|---|
| 1 | What is the product of 11 and 8? | 88 |
| 2 | How many lots of 0.6 are in 3.6? | 6 |
| 3 | What is one seventh of 3.5? | 0.5 |
| 4 | What is the difference between $(0.4 \times 8)$ and $(0.8 \times 4)$? | 0 |
| 5 | Find the sum of $(9 \times 0.3)$ and $(3 \times 1.1)$. | 6 |
| 6 | Share £5.60 equally among 7 boys. How much each? | 80p |
| 7 | Divide 84 by 7. | 12 |
| 8 | Thirty-two tenths is how many lots of 0.8? | 4 |
| 9 | 6 times 2 times 6 is | 72 |
| 10 | What is the remainder when 70 is divided by 8? | 6 |

## C

| | | ANSWER |
|---|---|---|
| 1 | A piece of string 4.8 m long is cut into 8 equal pieces. What is the length of one piece? | 60 cm |
| 2 | A bucket holds 8.1 litres of water, which is shared equally between 9 people. How many millilitres of water will they each get? | 900 ml |
| 3 | Eight biscuits cost 72p. How much do seven of the biscuits cost? | 63p |
| 4 | Three large floor tiles are placed side by side touching in a line. What is their total length? | |

| 0.6 m | 0.6 m | 0.6 m |
|---|---|---|

1.8 m

| | | ANSWER |
|---|---|---|
| 5 | Which of these numbers can be divided by both 5 and 12 without a remainder? [10, 12, 20, 24, 30, 50, 60, 72] | 60 |
| 6 | Chloe has £12. Hannah has seven times as much as that. Find the total of their money. | £96 |
| 7 | A line is split into parts in the ratio of 4:7. If the line is 55 cm long, what are the lengths of the two parts? | 20 cm   35 cm |
| 8 | The mean of 4 numbers is 0.4. Three of the numbers are 0.1, 0.8, 0.3. What is the fourth number? | 0.4 |
| 9 | 2.1 litres of oil fill 7 identical cups. How much does each hold? | 300 ml |
| 10 | What is the perimeter of a regular dodecagon with sides of 3 cm? | 36 cm |

25

# Section 2  Test 9

## A

| | | ANSWER |
|---|---|---|
| 1 | $4\overline{)3.2}$ | 0.8 |
| 2 | $11^2 =$ | 121 |
| 3 | $\frac{3}{4}$ of 360° is | 270° |
| 4 | $9 \times 8 \times 2 \times 0 =$ | 0 |
| 5 | 12p + 12p + 12p + 12p = | 48p |
| 6 | 5.4 kg ÷ 9 = | 0.6 kg |
| 7 | 5.6 ÷ 0.8 = | 7 |
| 8 | 0.6 × [    ] = 0.9 × 4 | 6 |
| 9 | 29 ÷ 5 = [    ] r [    ] | 5 r 4 |
| 10 | 4 × [  ] = £2.80 | £0.70 |

## B

| | | ANSWER |
|---|---|---|
| 1 | How many minutes are there in 8 hours? | 480 |
| 2 | What is one seventh of 42 cm? | 6 cm |
| 3 | 12 squared subtract 10 squared is | 44 |
| 4 | What is the product of 8 and 0.9? | 7.2 |
| 5 | How many months are there in 9 years? | 108 |
| 6 | Add (11 × 10) to (5 × 8) and divide by 3. | 50 |
| 7 | How many times heavier is 3.6 kg than 1.2 kg? | 3 |
| 8 | What number is equal to $8^2 + 4^2$? | 80 |
| 9 | Apples cost 12p each. How much will 8 cost? | 96p |
| 10 | Divide 68 by 11. | 6 r 2 |

## C

| | | ANSWE |
|---|---|---|
| 1 | Four note books cost £2.40. What will be the cost of 9 note books? | £5.4 |
| 2 | One ninth of a number is 0.3. What is the number? | 2. |
| 3 | Write the missing number. $9 \times 9 = 11 \times 8 - [\ \ ]$ | 7 |
| 4 | What is the smallest number which can be divided by both 12 and 9 without a remainder? | 3( |
| 5 | What is the perimeter of an equilateral triangle with sides of 0.6 cm? | 1.8 cr |
| 6 | A tin contains 0.4 kg of baked beans. Phil eats $\frac{1}{10}$ of the beans. What mass of beans does he eat? | 0.04 k |

| | | |
|---|---|---|
| 7 | A motorcyclist travels at 36 km per hour. How far does he ride in 10 minutes? | 6 kr |
| 8 | What is the mean of these 7 numbers? [10, 15, 6, 19, 2, 5, 6] | 9 |
| 9 | Seven kg cost £4.90. Find the price per kg. | £0.7 |
| 10 | A square mosaic tile has an area of 12 cm². Six tiles are used to make a shape, without gaps. What is the area of the shape? | 72 cm |

# Section 2  Test 10

| A | | ANSWER |
|---|---|---|
| 1 | $\frac{2}{3}$ of 360° is | 240° |
| 2 | 100 ÷ 11 = [ ] r [ ] | 9 r 1 |
| 3 | $(1^2 + 3^2) \times 7 =$ | 70 |
| 4 | 3.5 ÷ 5 = | 0.7 |
| 5 | 12⟌60 | 5 |
| 6 | 0.8 × [ ] = 3.2 | 4 |
| 7 | 0.7 × 0.9 = | 0.63 |
| 8 | $\frac{4}{9}$ of 36 cm is | 16 cm |
| 9 | $(3 \times 4) \times (2 \times 5) \times 6 =$ | 720 |
| 10 | The square of 12 cm is | 144 cm² |

| B | | ANSWER |
|---|---|---|
| 1 | Split 42 in the ratio of 3:4. | 18  24 |
| 2 | How many days in 12 weeks? | 84 |
| 3 | Multiply 8 by 0.9. | 7.2 |
| 4 | What is the total mass of 6 sets of 0.8 kg? | 4.8 kg |
| 5 | Divide 6.4 by 8. | 0.8 |
| 6 | What are three groups of 0.7? | 2.1 |
| 7 | There are eighty-one ninths. How many whole ones is that? | 9 |
| 8 | How many months are in 11 years? | 132 |
| 9 | What is the product of 7 and 0.8? | 5.6 |
| 10 | How many hours is 540 minutes? | 9 |

| C | | ANSWER |
|---|---|---|
| 1 | • stands for a missing sign, +, −, × or ÷. 1.2 × 6 = 8 • 0.8 What is the correct sign? | − |
| 2 | What is the perimeter of this regular pentagon? 0.9 cm | 4.5 cm |
| 3 | How many 9-litre cans can be filled from 63 litres of oil? | 7 |
| 4 | Sam has £11. Sara has 11 times as much as that. Find the total of their money. | £132 |
| 5 | Divide the total of 6.9 and 0.8 by 7. | 1.1 |
| 6 | Which of these numbers will divide into 108 without a remainder? [7, 8, 9, 10, 11] | 9 |
| 7 | This sector of a pie chart is one twelfth of the circle. What is the angle at the centre of the sector?  | 30° |
| 8 | A chocolate bar costs £0.70. How much change from £5 would you get if you bought 7 chocolate bars? | 10p |
| 9 | What is one sixth of the product of 8 and 9? | 12 |
| 10 | A rectangle has an area of 2.8 cm². Its width is 0.7 cm. What is its length? | 4 cm |

# Section 2   Test 11

## A

| | | ANSWER |
|---|---|---|
| 1 | $4 \times 0.7$ kg = | 2.8 kg |
| 2 | $(0.4 \div 5) \times (6 \times 0)$ = | 0 |
| 3 | $4.8 \div 1.2$ = | 4 |
| 4 | $[\ ]^2 = 64$ | 8 |
| 5 | $7.2 \div 9$ = | 0.8 |
| 6 | $(6 \times 2) \times [\ ] = 84$ | 7 |
| 7 | $[\ \ ] \div 11 = 11$ | 121 |
| 8 | 0.9 m + 0.9 m + 0.9 m = | 2.7 m |
| 9 | $\frac{3}{7}$ of 49 m is | 21 m |
| 10 | [   ] hours = 300 minutes | 5 |

## B

| | | ANSWER |
|---|---|---|
| 1 | Find the mean of 12, 9, 10, 17. | 12 |
| 2 | How much greater is 9 squared than 1 squared? | 80 |
| 3 | What is one sixth of 2.4 km? | 0.4 km |
| 4 | What number is equal to 0.8 times 6? | 4.8 |
| 5 | What is the product of 4 and 11? | 44 |
| 6 | How many times smaller is 70 than 350? | 5 |
| 7 | Multiply $(4 \times 3)$ by 9. | 108 |
| 8 | Share £5.40 equally between 6 boys. How much each? | £0.90 |
| 9 | How many quarters in 8? | 32 |
| 10 | How many months are there in 10 years? | 120 |

## C

| | | ANSW |
|---|---|---|
| 1 | When a number is divided by 3 the answer is 12. What is the number? | 3 |
| 2 | Trisha gave 5 friends 12 sweets each and she had 9 sweets left. How many did she have to start with? | 6 |
| 3 | One seventh of a number is 8. What is the number? | 5 |
| 4 | £96 is shared between Li and Sandeep. Li gets 7 times as much as Sandeep. How much does Li get? | £8 |
| 5 | Eight identical tins have a total mass of 5.6 kg. What is the mass of 6 of the tins? | 4.2 k |
| 6 | What is the total cost of 7 packets of chews and 3 packets of sweets? | |

| | | |
|---|---|---|
| | | 84 |
| 7 | A van can travel 9 km using one litre of petrol. How far can it travel using 0.9 litres? | 8.1 k |
| 8 | This line is 6 cm long. Another is 1.2 times longer. What is its length? | |
| | | 7.2 c |
| 9 | What is the difference between the number of days in 11 weeks and the months in 6 years? | 5 |
| 10 | What is the mean of these 8 numbers? [1, 0.5, 0.5, 0.2, 0.2, 0.2, 0.3, 0.3] | 0. |

28

# Section 2   Test 12

## A

| | | ANSWER |
|---|---|---|
| 1 | $\frac{8}{9}$ of 4.5 kg is | 4 kg |
| 2 | $1 \times 1 \times 1 \times 1 \times 1 \times 1 =$ | 1 |
| 3 | $[\ \ ]^2 = 121$ | 11 |
| 4 | £1.20 + £1.20 + £1.20 + £1.20 = | £4.80 |
| 5 | $99 \div 9 = [\ \ ] \div 12$ | 132 |
| 6 | $6.3 \div 0.7 =$ | 9 |
| 7 | $(6 \times 2) \times (4 \times 3) =$ | 144 |
| 8 | $6^2 \div 9 =$ | 4 |
| 9 | $\frac{5}{9}$ of 180° is | 100° |
| 10 | $[\ \ ] \div 12 = 6$ | 72 |

## B

| | | ANSWER |
|---|---|---|
| 1 | Twice 12 = 3 times [ ] | 8 |
| 2 | Split 56 in the ratio of 3:4. | 24  32 |
| 3 | What is the product of 0.6 and 7? | 4.2 |
| 4 | How many times heavier is 2.8 kg than 0.4 kg? | 7 |
| 5 | Divide 2.4 by 4. | 0.6 |
| 6 | How many months are there in 8 years? | 96 |
| 7 | There are twenty-five fifths. How many whole ones is that? | 5 |
| 8 | What is 7 squared plus 3 squared? | 58 |
| 9 | Which number, other than 1, 2, 3, 4, 6, 12 and 24, divides exactly into 24? | 8 |
| 10 | By how much is $\frac{5}{8}$ of 48 greater than $\frac{8}{9}$ of 27? | 6 |

## C

| | | ANSWER |
|---|---|---|
| 1 | Eighty-four chairs are arranged in rows of 12. How many rows? | 7 |
| 2 | On a clock-face, what is the angle between the hands when the time is 1 o'clock?  | 30° |
| 3 | A pencil costs £0.60 and a paintbrush costs £1.20. How much will it cost in total to buy 3 pencils and 5 paintbrushes? | £7.80 |
| 4 | What number, when multiplied by 5, will give a product of 2.0? | 0.4 |
| 5 | Divide the total of 1.7 and 0.4 by 3. | 0.7 |
| 6 | The angles in this diagram are equal. What is the size of angle $x$? | 120° |
| 7 | A line is split into parts in the ratio of 3:8. If the line is 88 cm long, what are the lengths of the two parts? | 24 cm  64 cm |
| 8 | The mean of 6 numbers is 9. Five of the numbers are 5, 5, 10, 10, 20. What is the sixth number? | 4 |
| 9 | What is the perimeter of a regular nonagon with sides of 0.9 cm? | 8.1 cm |
| 10 | The square root of a number is 2 more than the square root of 100. What is the number? | 144 |

# Progress Test 2

Write the numbers 1 to 20 down the side of a sheet of paper.
Write alongside these numbers the **answers only** to the following questions.
Work as quickly as you can.
Time allowed – **10 minutes.**

| 1 | $400\,g \times 8 =$ | **3200** g |
|---|---|---|
| 2 | What is $\frac{3}{7}$ of 28? | **12** |
| 3 | $60 \div 9 = [\quad]\,r\,[\quad]$ | **6 r 6** |
| 4 | $[\quad]^2 = 49$ | **7** |
| 5 | What is the product of 0.6 and 7? | **4.2** |
| 6 | How long will it take to travel a distance of 36 km travelling at 4 km/h? | **9 h** |
| 7 | $80 \times 3 = 4 \times [\quad]$ | **60** |

8    A bar of chocolate has 18 chunks. Edgar eats $\frac{1}{3}$ of the bar. How many chunks does he eat?     **6**

| 9 | Split £56 in the ratio of 3:5. | **£21, £35** |
|---|---|---|

10    The distance from Matby to Clew is one eighth of the distance from Clew to Skern. How far it is from Matby to Skern via Clew? 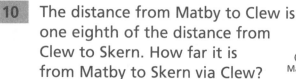    **7.2 km**

| 11 | What is 12 squared subtract 6 squared? | **108** |
|---|---|---|
| 12 | What is the remainder when 111 is divided by 11? | **1** |
| 13 | The mean of 6 numbers is 8. Five of the numbers are 5, 5, 10, 10, 15. What is the sixth number? | **3** |

14    A tin contains 6.3 litres of oil. Simon uses one seventh of the oil. How much is left?     **5.4 litres**

| 15 | What is the difference between $(0.9 \times 9)$ and $(1.1 \times 11)$? | **4** |
|---|---|---|
| 16 | A bucket holds 8.4 litres of water, which is shared equally between 7 people. How many millilitres of water will they each get? | **1200** ml |
| 17 | Nine bricks have a mass of 2.7 kg. How many bricks have a mass of 3.6 kg? | **12** |
| 18 | The perimeter of a square is 160 mm. What is its area in square millimetres? | **1600** mm² |

19    The shaded sector shown is five sixths of the circle. What is the angle of the sector?     **300°**

| 20 | Divide the difference between $10^2$ and $2^2$ by 12. | **8** |
|---|---|---|

u will work through Progress Test 2 at **four** different times. When you first work the test
a) colour the first column to show the number of examples correct out of 20
b) enter the date.
ch time you work the test, enter the result and the date in the marked columns.

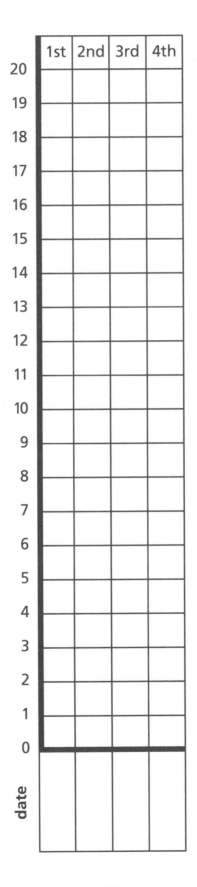